90's HITS

easy playalong *for* recorder

WISE PUBLICATIONS
London / New York / Paris / Sydney / Copenhagen / Madrid / Tokyo

Exclusive Distributors:
Music Sales Limited
8/9 Frith Street,
London W1V 5TZ, England.

Music Sales Pty Limited
120 Rothschild Avenue,
Rosebery, NSW 2018,
Australia.

Order No. AM959959
ISBN 0-7119-7805-0
This book © Copyright 2000 by Wise Publications.

Music compiled and arranged by Paul Honey.
Music processed by Enigma Music Production Services.
Cover photography courtesy George Taylor.
Printed in the United Kingdom by
Printwise (Haverhill) Limited, Haverhill, Suffolk.

CD produced by Paul Honey.
Instrumental solos by Andy Finden.
All guitars by Arthur Dick.
Engineered by Kester Sims.

Your Guarantee of Quality:
As publishers, we strive to produce every book to
the highest commercial standards.
The music has been freshly engraved and the book
has been carefully designed to minimise awkward page
turns and to make playing from it a real pleasure.
Particular care has been given to specifying acid-free,
neutral-sized paper made from pulps which have not
been elemental chlorine bleached.
This pulp is from farmed sustainable forests and
was produced with special regard for the environment.
Throughout, the printing and binding have been planned
to ensure a sturdy, attractive publication which should
give years of enjoyment.
If your copy fails to meet our high standards,
please inform us and we will gladly replace it.

Music Sales' complete catalogue describes
thousands of titles and is available in full colour
sections by subject, direct from Music Sales Limited.
Please state your areas of interest and send
a cheque/postal order for £1.50 for postage to:
Music Sales Limited, Newmarket Road,
Bury St. Edmunds, Suffolk IP33 3YB.

www.musicsales.com

Junior Guest Spot

RECORDER FINGERING CHART

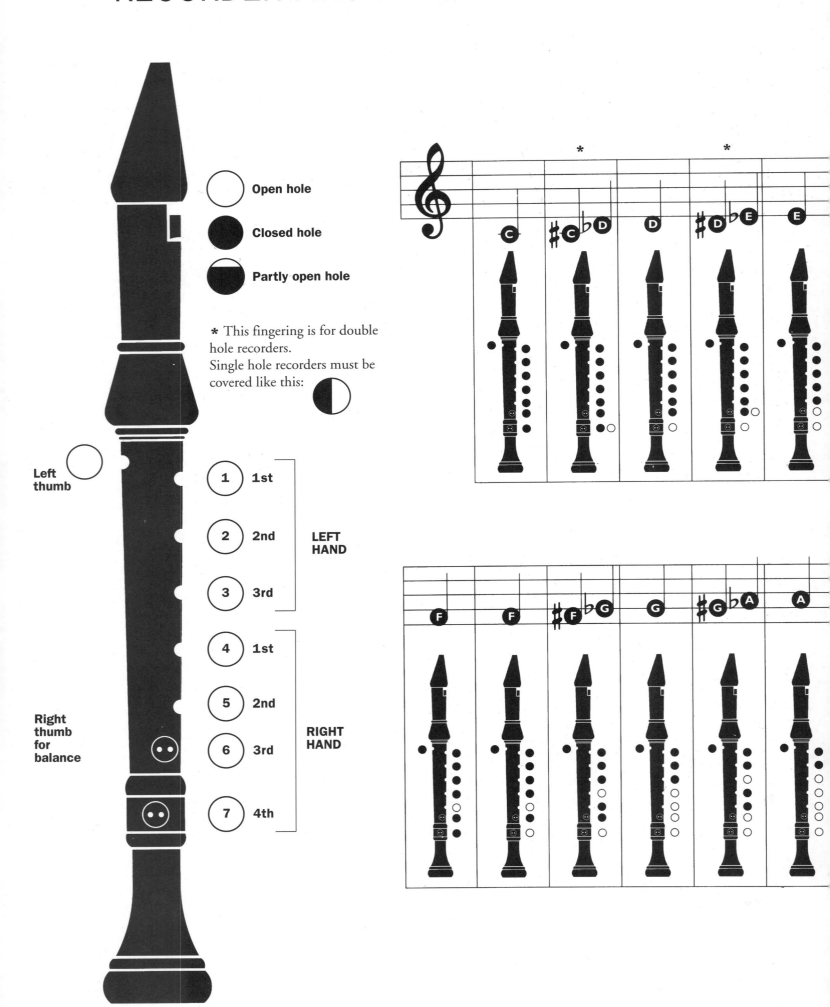

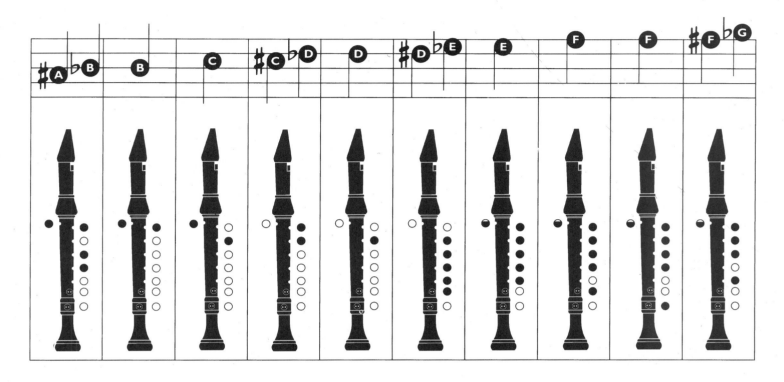
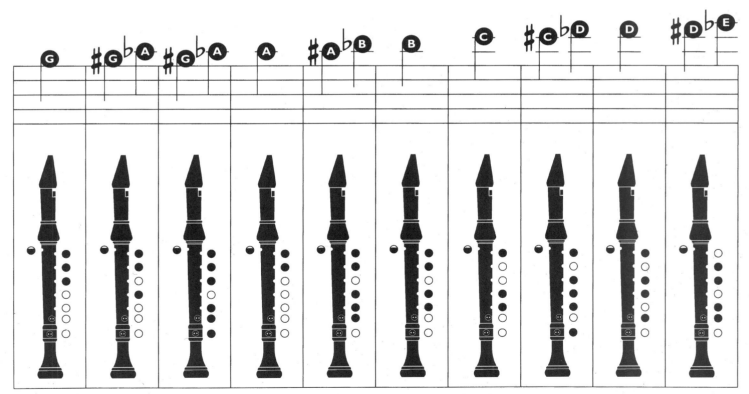

ANGELS

Words & Music by Robbie Williams & Guy Chambers

Rather slow

I sit and wait,___ does an

an - gel con - tem - plate my fate, and do they know___

___ the pla - ces where we go when we're grey and

old. 'Cos I have been___ told that sal -

- va - tion lets their wings un - fold. So when I'm

ly - ing in my bed, thoughts run - ning through my head I

feel that love is dead, I'm lov - ing an - gels in - stead.

And through it all_____ she of - fers me__ pro - tec -

- tion, a lot of love and af - fec - tion whe - ther I'm right or

wrong. And down the wa - ter - fall where - ev - er it may

take me I know that life won't break me when I come__ to call

she won't for - sake me, I'm lov - ing an - gels in - stead.__

__ And through it all I'm lov - ing an - gels in - stead.__

7

BEAUTIFUL STRANGER

Words & Music by Madonna & William Orbit

HIGH

Words by Paul Tucker
Music by Paul Tucker & Tunde Baiyewu

Moderately

And we'll won - der_____ how we made it through the

night, at the end of the day re - mem - ber the way we stayed so__ close 'til the end,

but re - mem - ber_____ it was me and you. 'Cause we are gon - na

be for - ev - er you and me, you will al - ways keep me fly__

__ ing__ high in the sky of love.__ 'Cause we are gon-na

be for - ev - er you and me, you will al - ways keep me fly__

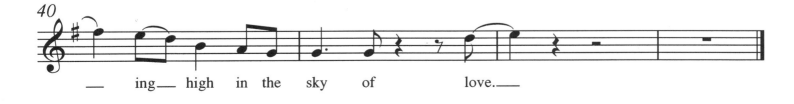

__ ing__ high in the sky of love.__

I HAVE A DREAM

Words & Music by Benny Andersson & Björn Ulvaeus

Moderately

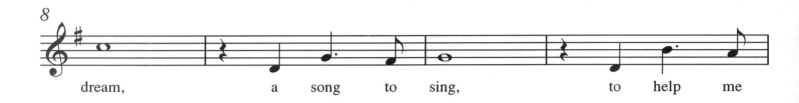

dream,   a song to sing,   to help me

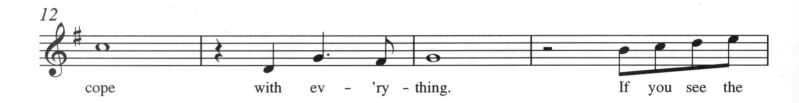

cope   with ev – 'ry – thing.   If you see the

won – der   of a fai – ry tale   you can take

— the fu – ture   ev – en if you fail.   I be – lieve in

an – gels,   some – thing good in ev – 'ry – thing— I—

see. I be-lieve in an - gels, when I know the time— is right— for—

me, I'll cross the stream, I have a dream. I be-lieve in

an - gels, some-thing good in ev - - 'ry-thing— I—

see. I be - lieve in an - gels, when I know the

time— is right— for— me, I'll cross the stream, I have a

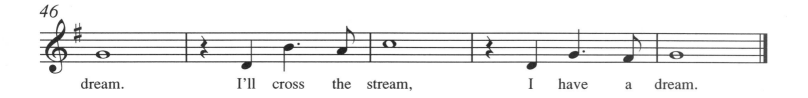

dream. I'll cross the stream, I have a dream.

I WANT IT THAT WAY

Words & Music by Max Martin & Andreas Carlsson

Moderately

why; I ne-ver wan-na hear you say_____ "I want it that way."_ Am

I your fi - re?__ Your one de - si - re?__ Yes I

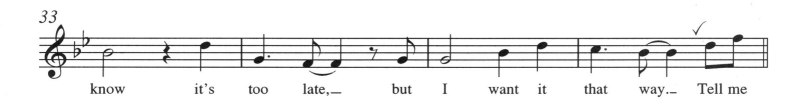

know it's too late,_ but I want it that way._ Tell me

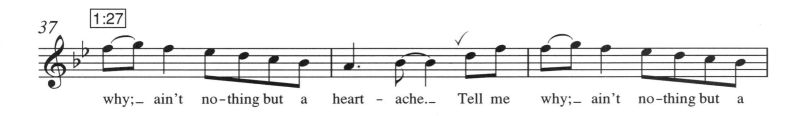

why;_ ain't no-thing but a heart - ache._ Tell me why;_ ain't no-thing but a

mis - take._ Tell me why; I ne-ver wan-na hear you say_____

"I want it that way."_ I want it that way.

I BELIEVE I CAN FLY

Words & Music by R. Kelly

I WILL ALWAYS LOVE YOU

Words & Music by Dolly Parton

LOVE IS ALL AROUND

Words & Music by Reg Presley

Moderately

I feel it in my fin-gers, I feel it in my

toes. The love that's all a-round me and so the feel-ing

grows. It's writ-ten on the wind, it's ev-'ry-where I

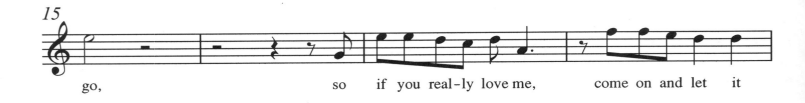

go, so if you real-ly love me, come on and let it

show. You know I love you, I al-ways will.

My mind's made up by the way that I feel. There's

no be-gin-ning, there'll be no— end,— 'cause on my— love you

can de - pend.—
I

feel it in my fin-gers, I feel it in my toes.

The love that's all a-round me and so the feel-ing

grows. It's writ-ten on the wind,

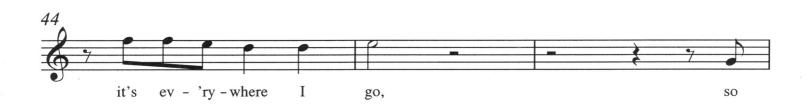

it's ev-'ry-where I go, so

if you real-ly love me, come on and let it show.

LOVEFOOL

Words & Music by Peter Svensson & Nina Persson

Brightly

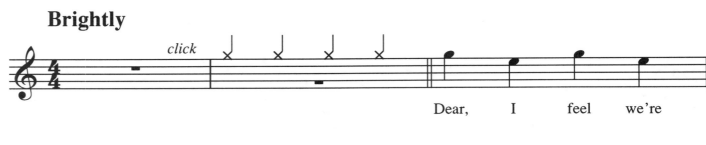

Dear, I feel we're

fac - ing a prob - lem, you love me no long - er, I know and

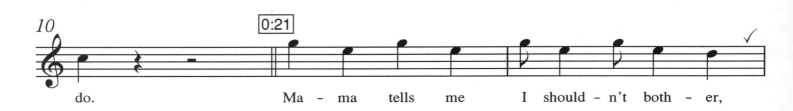

may - be there is no - thing that I can do to make you

do. Ma - ma tells me I should - n't both - er,

that I ought to stick to an - oth - er man, a man who

sure - ly de - serves me I think you do.

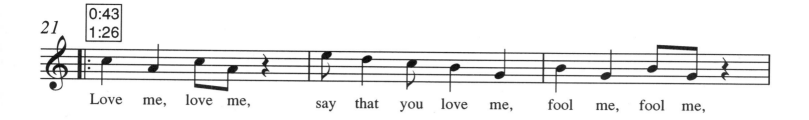

Love me, love me, say that you love me, fool me, fool me,

go on and fool me, love me, love me, pre - tend that you love me,

leave me, leave me, just say___ that you need me. So I

cry. And I beg for you to

love me, love me, say that you love me, leave me, leave me, just

say that you need me, I can't care a - bout an - y - thing but

you. an - y - thing but you.

MARVELLOUS

Words & Music by Ian Broudie

Not too fast

Oh— you hope to fit but you're fit

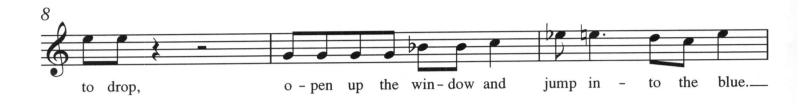

to drop, o - pen up the win - dow and jump in - to the blue.—

Things could be mar-vel -lous, things could be

fa- bu -lous. D'you need a push, I'll push— you off,

o - pen up the win-dow and jump in - to the blue.—

Things could be mar-vel-lous soon.— Oh, well these are the

days, this is the life, there'll al-ways be some-thing on your

mind you'll ne-ver quite find. Won't you ev - er make your mind up?

Oh well these are the days and this is the life, there'll al-ways be

some-thing on your mind you'll ne-ver quite find. You used to know but

now you for-got-ten, a sub-ma-rine got stuck to the bot-tom. These are the days so

wake up 'cause this is the time, and you know— I'm— right.

PERFECT MOMENT

Words & Music by James Marr & Wendy Page

Slowly

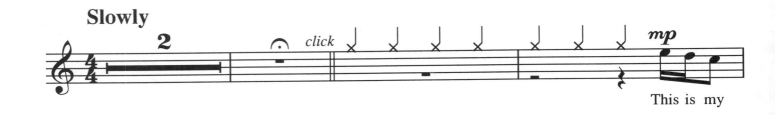

mo -ment,   this is my per - fect mo - ment with____ you.

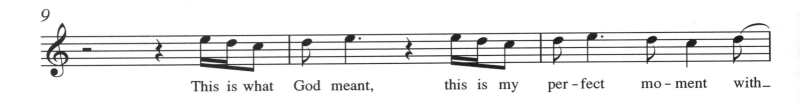

This is what God meant, this is my per - fect mo - ment with_

____ you. Wish I could freeze this space in

time, the way that I feel__ for you in - side.____ This is my

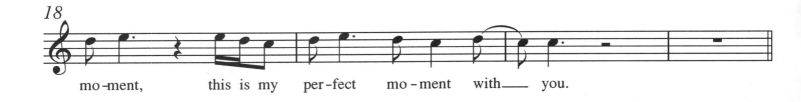

mo - ment, this is my per - fect mo - ment with____ you.

Tell me you love me, when you leave, you're more than a sha-dow,

that's what I believe. You take me to pla-ces I ne-ver thought I'd see.

Min-ute by min-ute you're the world to me. I wish I could frame the look in your

eyes, the way that I feel, for you in-side. This is my

mo-ment, this is my per-fect mo-ment with you. This is my

mo-ment, this is my per-fect mo-ment with you.

SEARCH FOR THE HERO

Words & Music by Mike Pickering & Paul Heard

Moderately

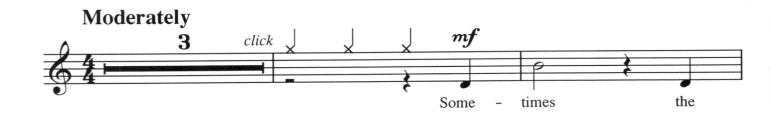

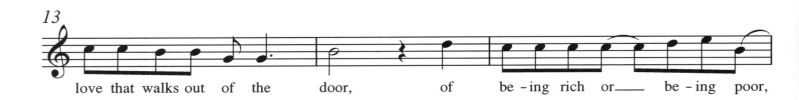

then that faith ar-rives, to make you feel at least a - live,___ and that's

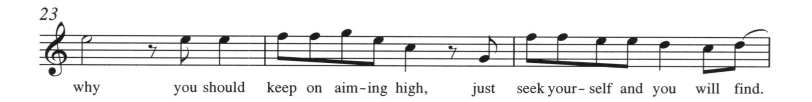

why you should keep on aim-ing high, just seek your-self and you will find.

You've got to search for the rea - son in - side your-self,

search for the se - crets you hide.___ Search for the he - ro in - side

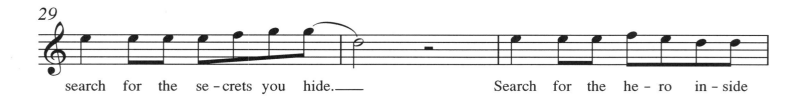

your - self, un - til you find the key to your

life. You've got to - til you find the key to your life.

SO YOUNG

Words & Music by Andrea Corr, Caroline Corr, Sharon Corr & Jim Corr

And when to-mor-row comes, we can do it all a-gain.

Yeah we are so young now, we are so young, so young now.

And when to-mor-row comes we'll just do it all a-gain.

1:28

mf

Yeah, yeah, yeah, yeah,

yeah. Yeah, yeah, yeah, yeah,

yeah. Yeah, yeah, yeah, yeah, yeah.

Yeah, yeah, yeah, yeah, yeah.

STOP

Words & Music by Victoria Aadams, Emma Bunton, Melanie Brown,
Melanie Chisholm, Geri Halliwell, Andy Watkins & Paul Wilson

Brightly

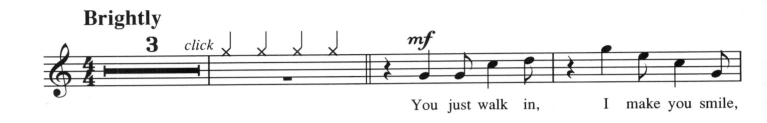

You just walk in,   I make you smile,

it's cool but   you don't ev - en know   me.___   You take an inch,

I run a mile.   Can't win, you're   al - ways right be -hind   me.___

And we know that you could   go and find some oth - er,   take or leave it or just

don't ev -en both - er.___   Caught in a craze,   it's just a phase,   or will this

be a-round for ev - er?___ Don't you know it's go - in' too fast,

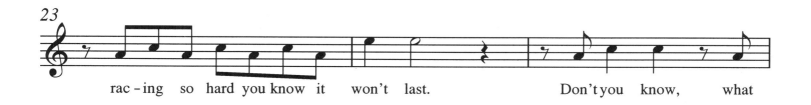

rac -ing so hard you know it won't last. Don't you know, what

can't you see, Slow it down, read the sign, so you know just where you're go - in'.

Stop right now, thank you ve - ry much. I need some - bo - dy with a

hu - man touch._____ Hey you, al - ways on the run. Got - ta

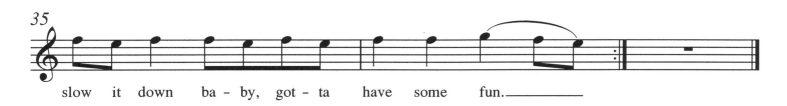

slow it down ba - by, got - ta have some fun._____

NO MATTER WHAT

Words by Jim Steinman
Music by Andrew Lloyd Webber

1/03 (46350)